breeze-easy method 1
Clarinet

by Valentine Anzalone

© 1958, 1984 WARNER BROS. INC.
All Rights Reserved

Cover photo courtesy of the Selmer Company.

FOREWORD

This METHOD offers to the young student a systematic approach to correct concepts in music reading, and clarinet playing. The method may be used with equally satisfying results either for private study or for class work. The fundamentals of tone production, technique, rhythmic understanding, and tonal consciousness have been especially emphasized. Additionally, this book offers a refreshing repertoire of new song material that will delight both student and teacher.

Through this course of study in which efficiency and thoroughness have been pin-pointed, the student is guided to take his place as a contributing member of the school band or orchestra in the shortest possible time. Upon completion of books I & II of the "BREEZE EASY" METHOD for CLARINET, the student will be prepared to enter directly into most intermediate clarinet methods.

Valentine C. Angalone

PLAYING POSITIONS

PROPER HAND & FINGER POSITION

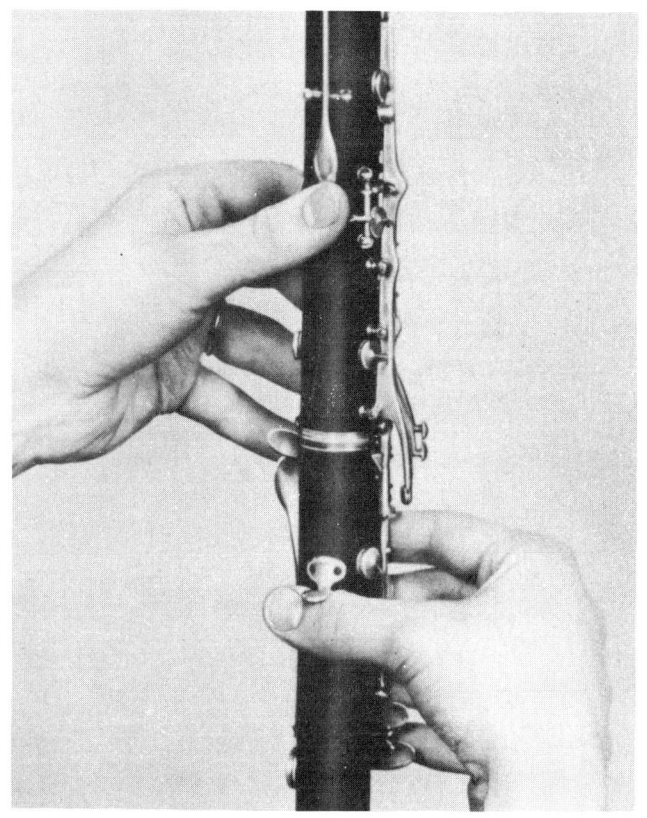

THE THUMBS IN PLAYING POSITION

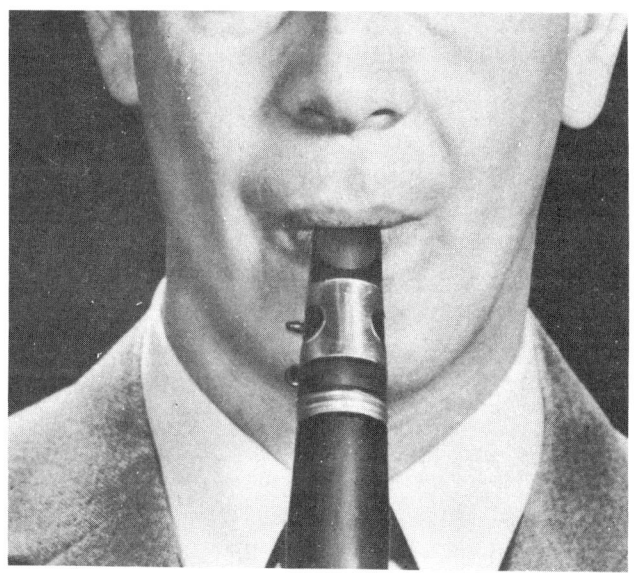

LIPS & MOUTHPIECE IN CORRECT
PLAYING POSITION

HOW TO READ THE FINGERING GIVEN IN THIS BOOK

The Clarinet has 7 holes which may be closed by the fingers.

This sign — ● — tells us that the hole is to be covered.

This sign — ○ — tells us that the hole is kept open.

When a key is to be pressed, its number or letter will be given.

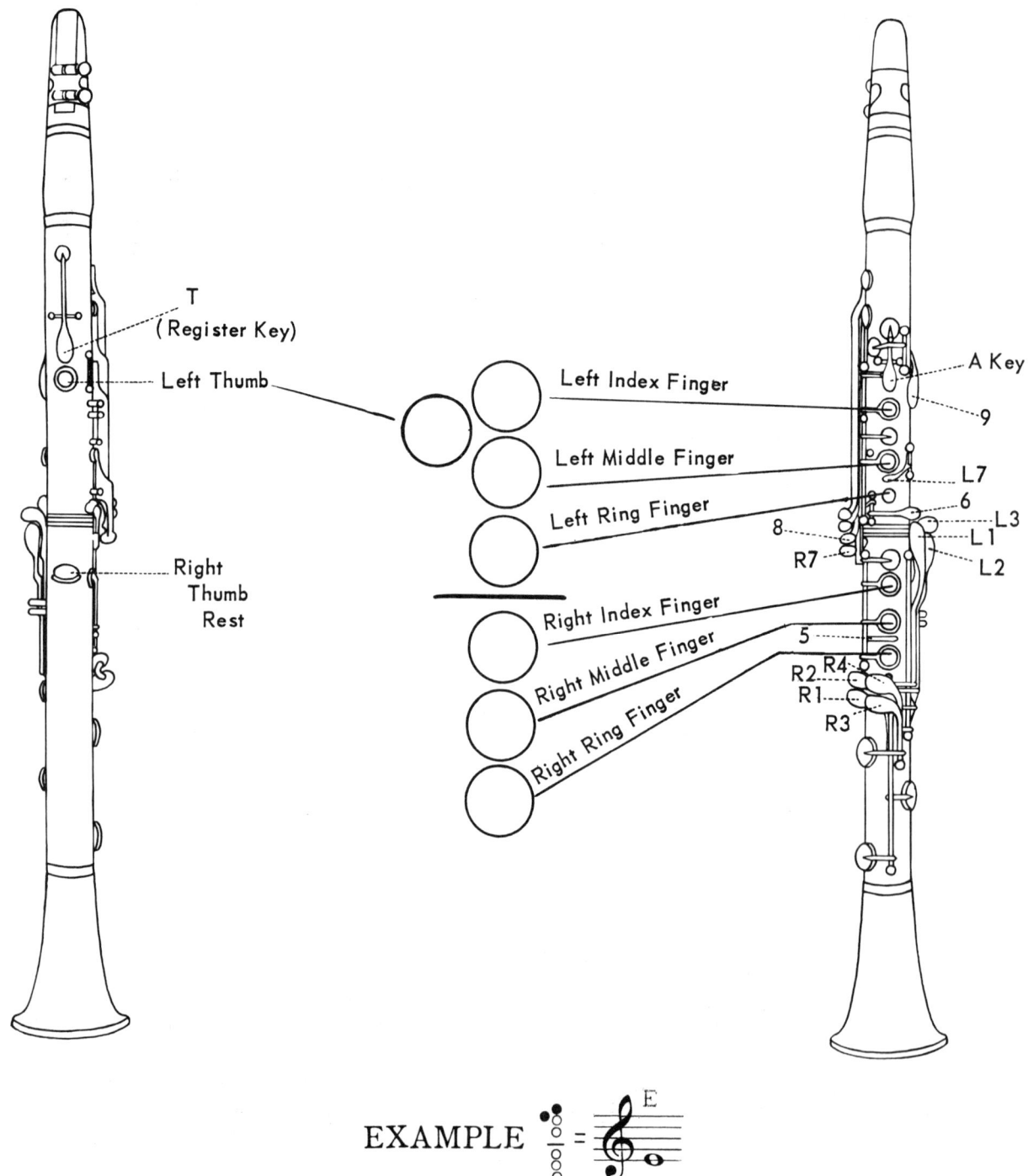

EXAMPLE

The fingering diagram in the example above indicates that you should close the left thumb hole and close the first hole with the left index finger.

(A FINGERING CHART for general reference is given on pages 30 and 31.)

© 1958 WARNER BROS. INC.
All Rights Reserved

PRELIMINARY LESSON

THINGS YOU SHOULD KNOW BEFORE WE BEGIN:

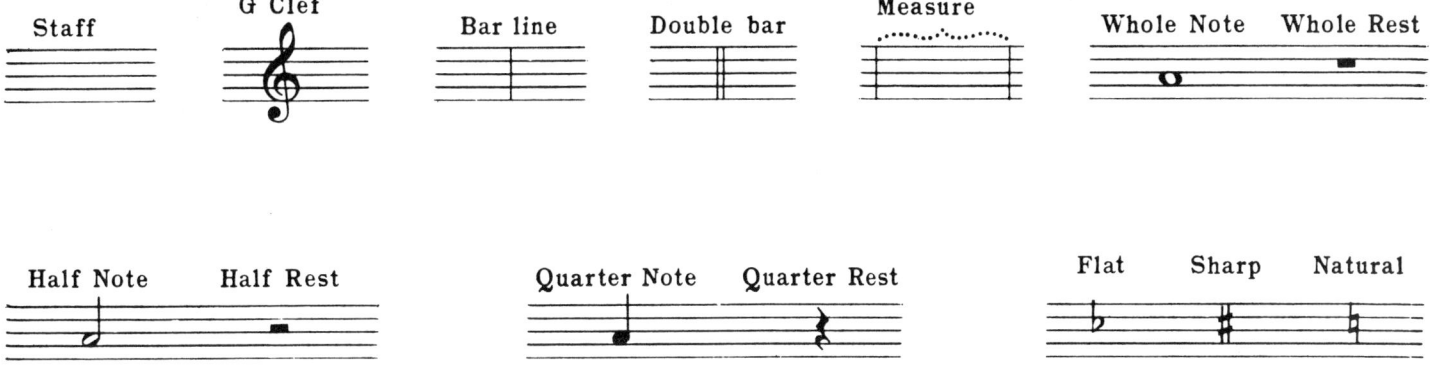

TIME SIGNATURES

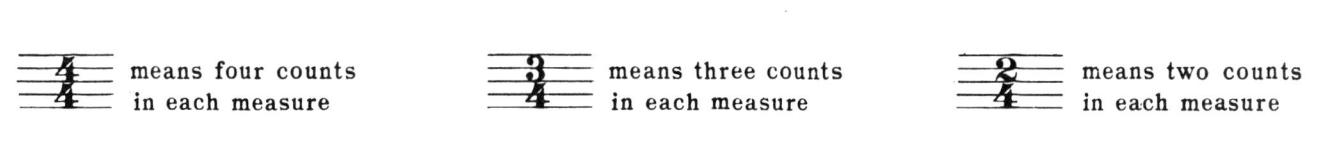

NAMES OF NOTES

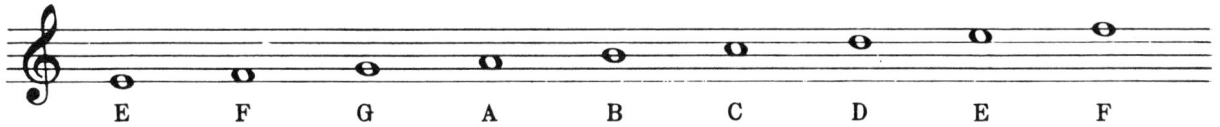

OUR FIRST TONES

DO NOT PUFF OUT YOUR CHEEKS!

YOUR TEACHER WILL SHOW YOU HOW TO HOLD YOUR INSTRUMENT AND PRODUCE A TONE CORRECTLY. PRACTICE HOLDING EACH OF THE FIRST TONES FOR A LONG WHILE. KEEP TRYING TO IMPROVE YOUR TONE BY LISTENING TO YOURSELF.

21389-29

LESSON 2.

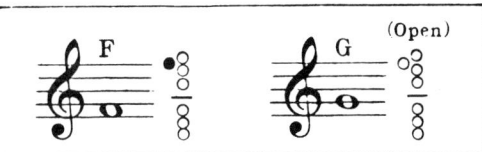

1.

2.

3.

4.

5.

6.

7.

8.

9.

FIRST DUET

10.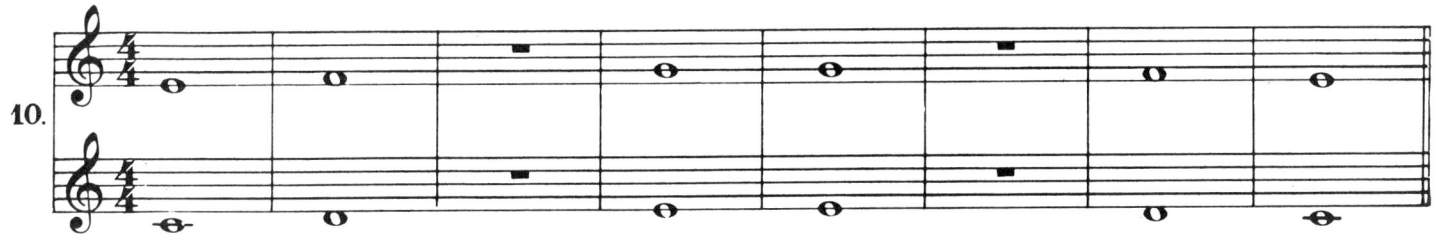

THIS LESSON HAS BEEN COMPLETED.   DATE _____   EXCELLENT ☐ GOOD ☐ FAIR ☐

21389-29

LESSON 9.

= SLUR ♮ = NATURAL SIGN
PICK-UP NOTE

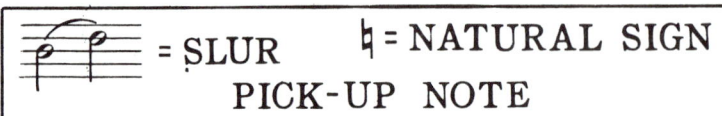

THE F SCALE (Memorize)
NOTICE THE KEY SIGN
1.
SLURRED NOTES
New
2.
CONNECT THESE TWO TONES
3.
CONNECT THESE FOUR TONES
New
THIS CANCELS THE FLAT
4.
5.
ABIDE WITH ME
6.
DUKE STREET
7.
New
PICK-UP NOTE
ON TOP OF OLD SMOKEY
8.
COUNT: 3 1 2 3 1 2 3 1 2 3
1 2

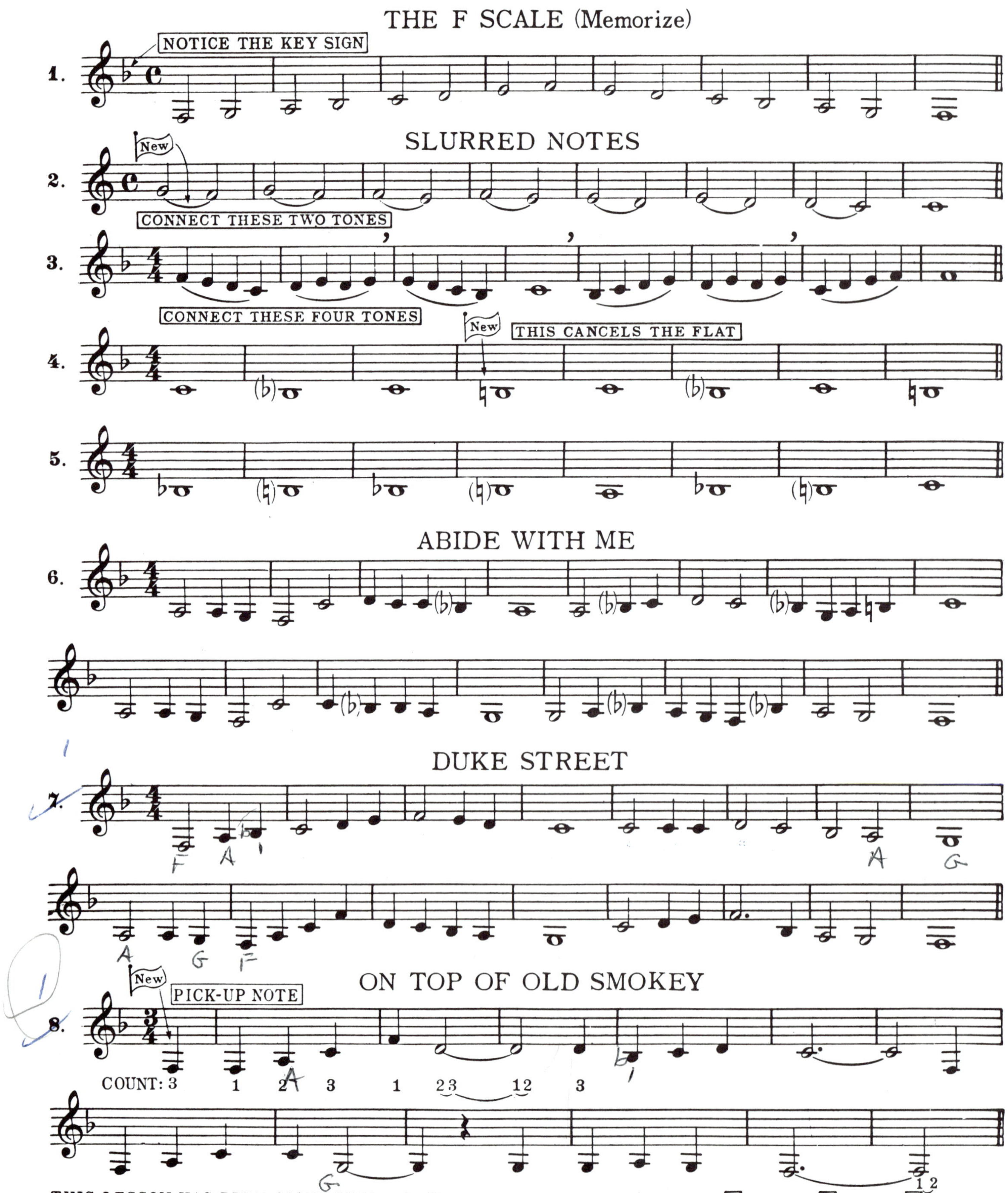

THIS LESSON HAS BEEN COMPLETED. DATE ______________ EXCELLENT ☐ GOOD ☐ FAIR ☐

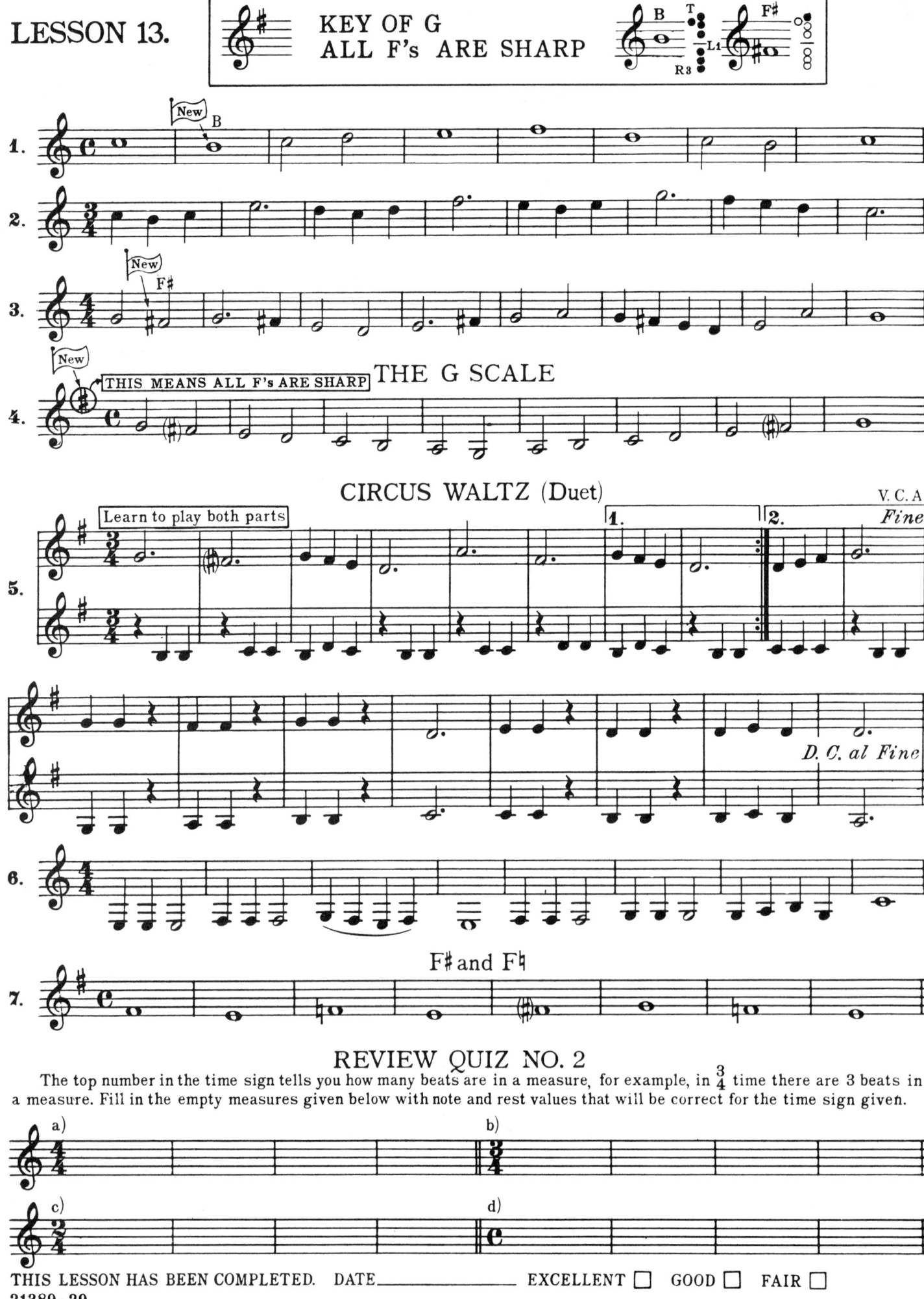

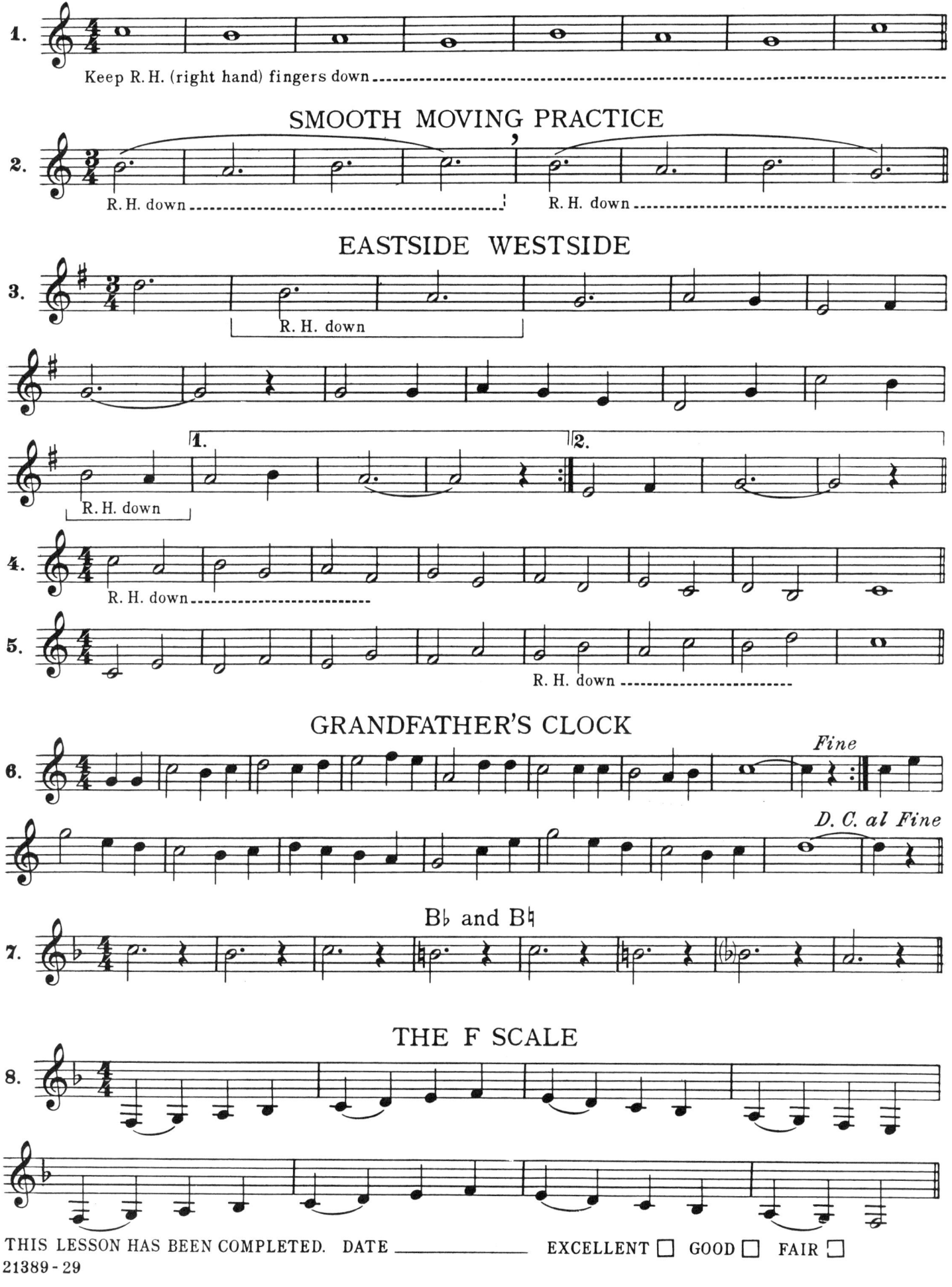

LESSON 16.

>= ACCENT MARK

D. S. al Fine - Go back to the sign (𝄋) and play to *Fine* (End).

ACCENT EXERCISE

1.

GOING HOME (Duet)

DVORAK

2.

AFTER-BEATS

3.

AT THE BOTTOM OF THE DEEP (Waltz)

V. C. A.

4.

5.

POODLES ON PARADE

V. C. A.

6.

SCALE IN THIRDS

7.

THIS LESSON HAS BEEN COMPLETED. DATE ________ EXCELLENT ☐ GOOD ☐ FAIR ☐

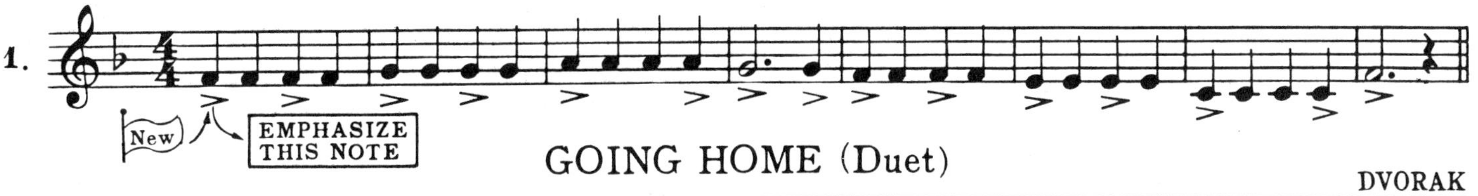

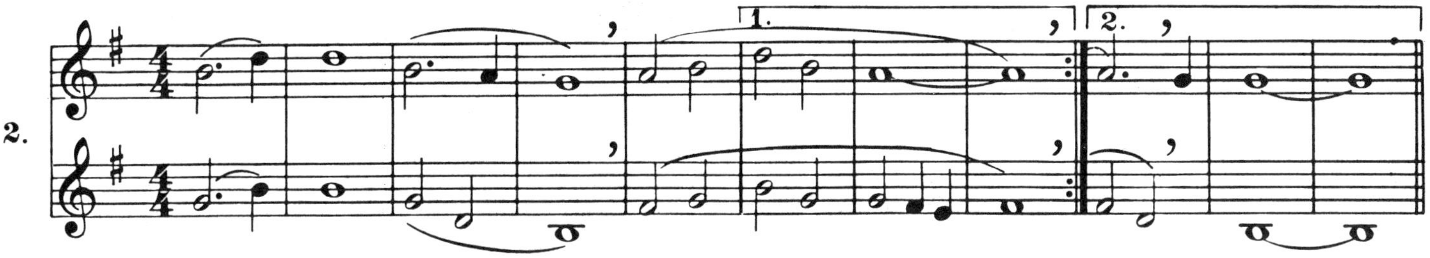

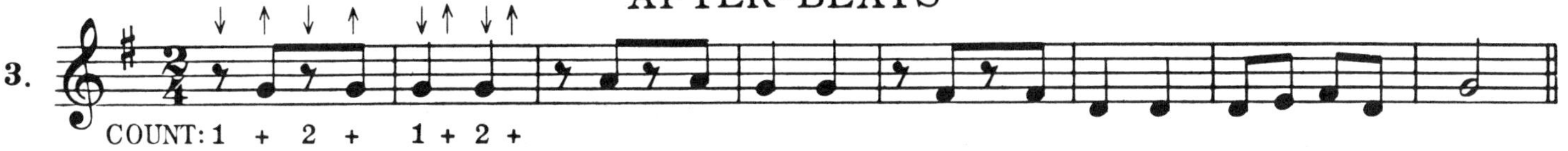

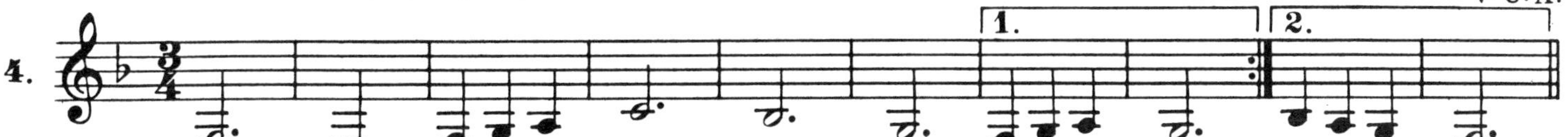

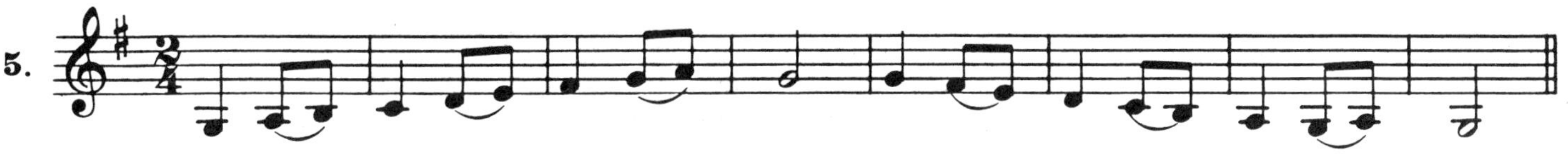

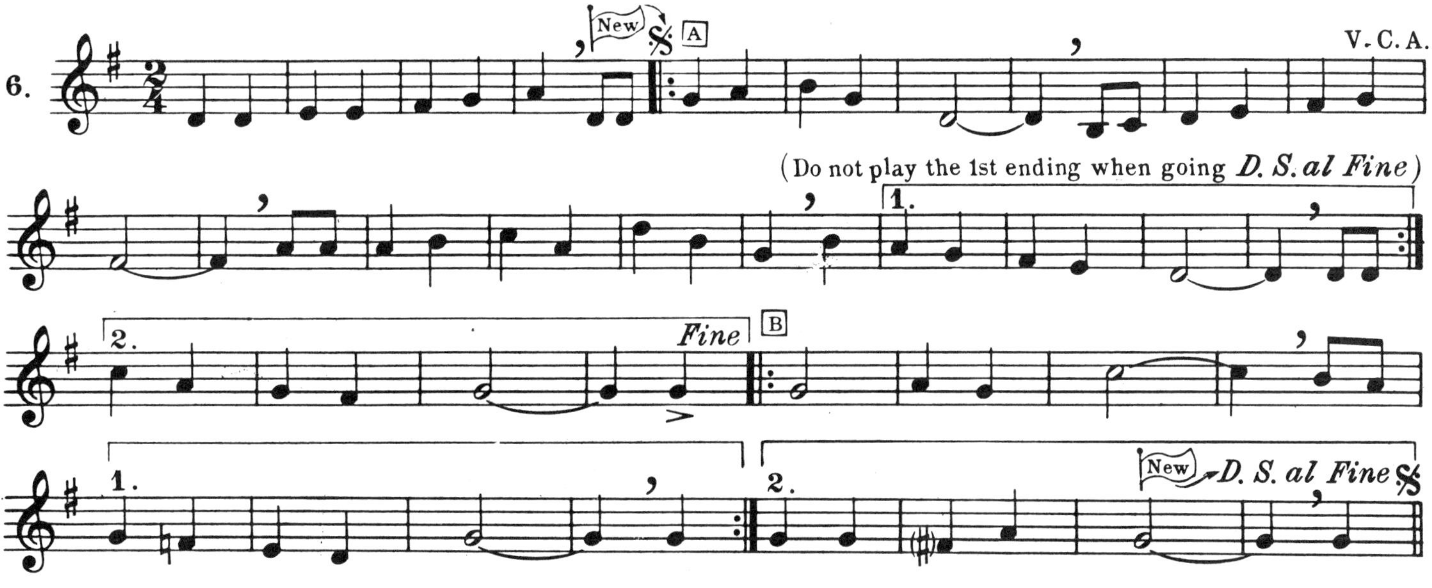

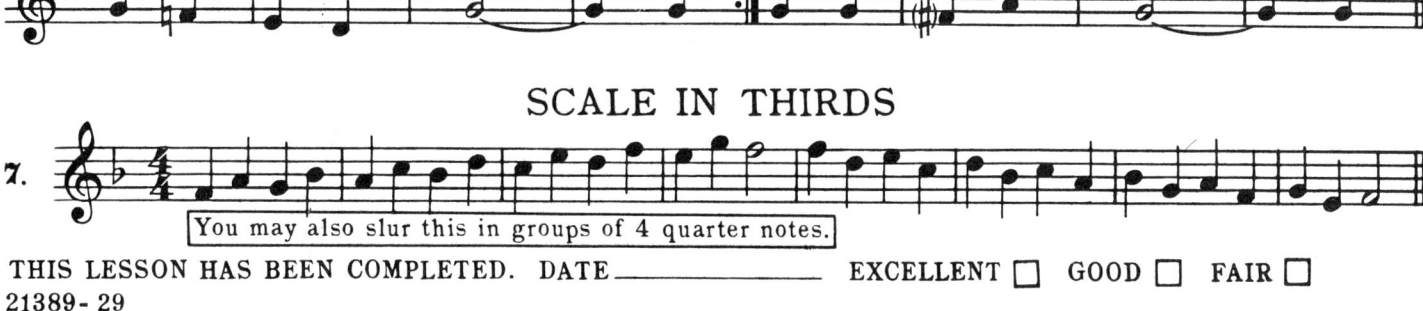

22

LESSON 17.

= REST 2 CONSECUTIVE MEASURES

LESSON 18.

p = SOFT
f = LOUD
= STACCATO - Detached Tones

A SCOTCH MELODY

THE ECHO SONG

V. C. A.

THE STACCATO

MEASURES 1 & 2 SHOULD SOUND ALIKE BECAUSE OF THE STACCATO MARKS IN MEASURE 2

AMARYLLIS

GHYS

CHROMATIC SONG

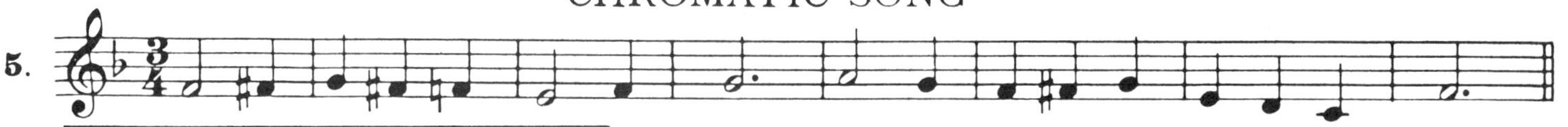

Ask your teacher how to finger this song.

TECHNICAL EXERCISES

IN TECHNICAL EXERCISES (Numbers 6 & 7), START SLOWLY AND GO FASTER AS YOU LEARN EACH LINE.

Repeat many times.

Repeat many times.

MELODY BY HAYDN

THIS LESSON HAS BEEN COMPLETED. DATE ________ EXCELLENT ☐ GOOD ☐ FAIR ☐

LESSON 19.

♩. = DOTTED QUARTER NOTE

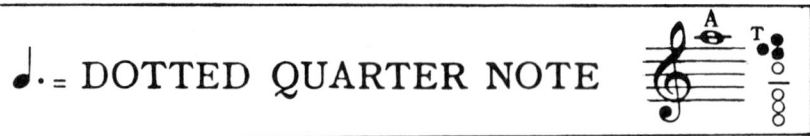

INTRODUCING THE DOTTED QUARTER NOTE

1.
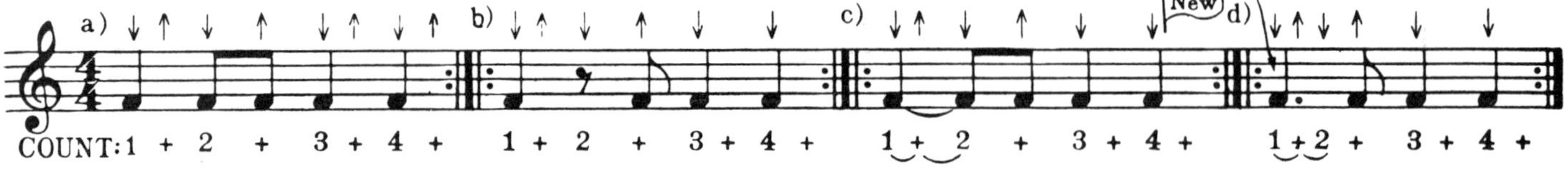

2.
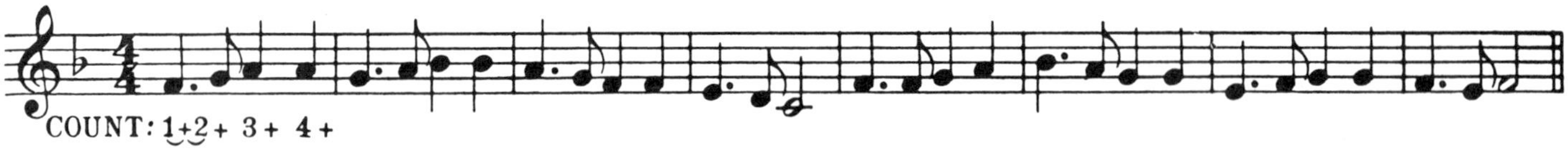

ALMA MATER

3.
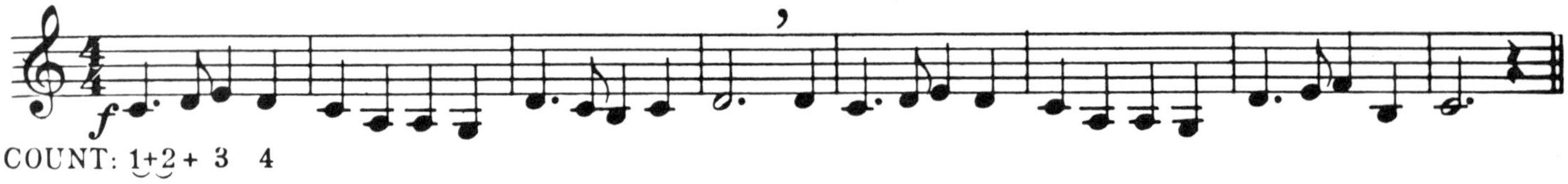

PATRIOTIC HYMN

4.
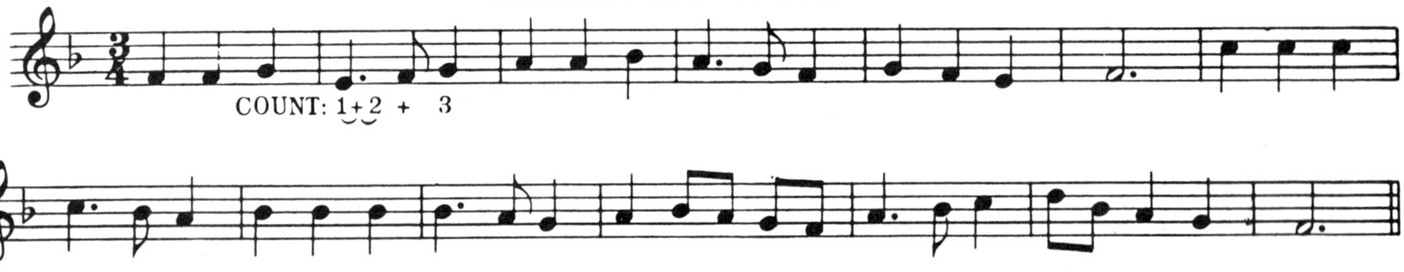

SLURRING EXERCISE

5.
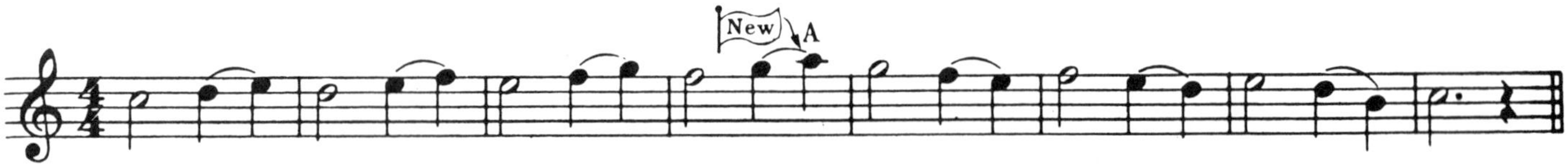

6.
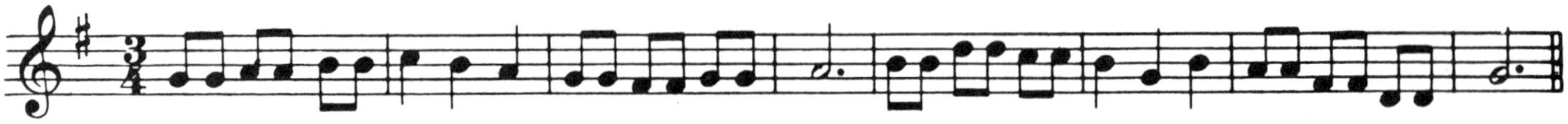

O COME ALL YE FAITHFUL

PLAY BOTH PARTS

7.
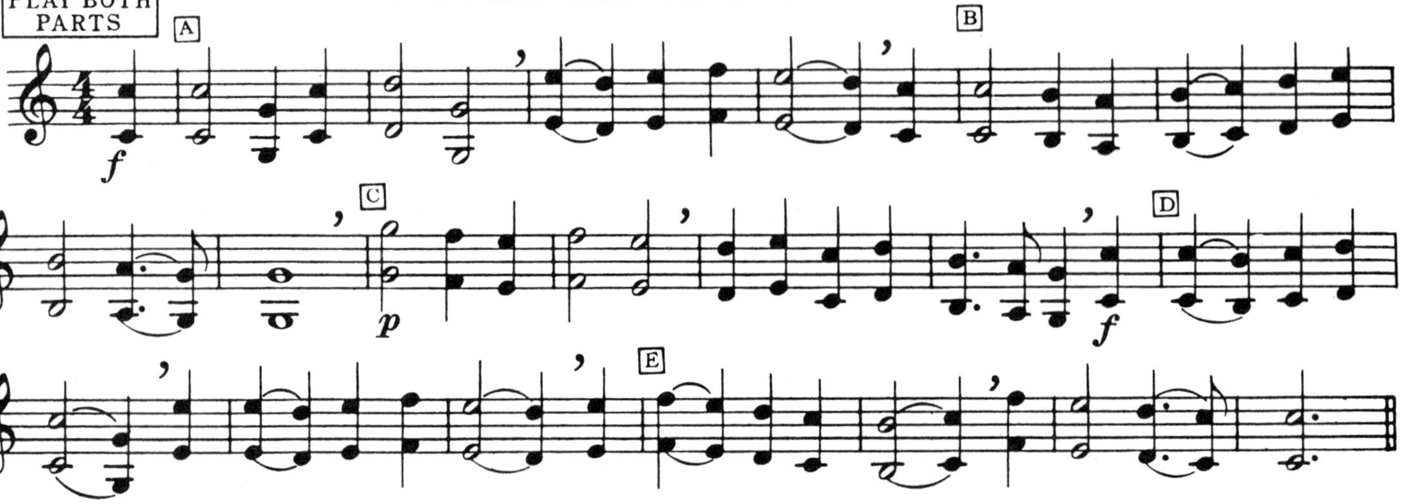

THIS LESSON HAS BEEN COMPLETED. DATE__________ EXCELLENT ☐ GOOD ☐ FAIR ☐

LESSON 20.

G MAJOR SCALE AND CHORD PRACTICE (Memorize)

MELODY FROM BEETHOVEN'S 9th SYMPHONY (Duet)

THE STAR SPANGLED BANNER

STACCATO EXERCISE

THIS LESSON HAS BEEN COMPLETED. DATE _____ EXCELLENT ☐ GOOD ☐ FAIR ☐

LESSON 21.

KEY OF B FLAT
ALL B's AND E's ARE FLAT

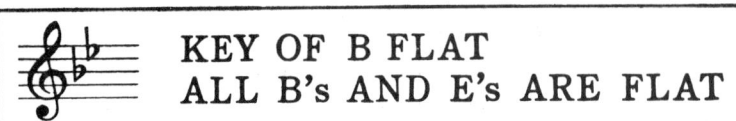

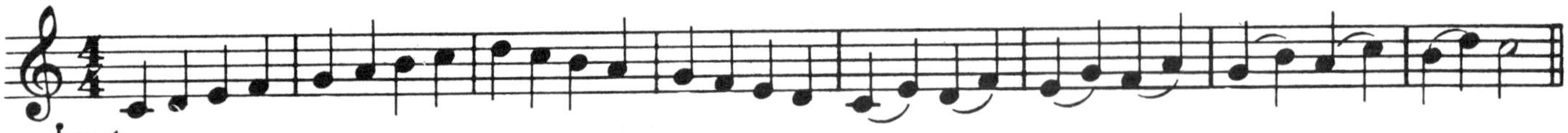

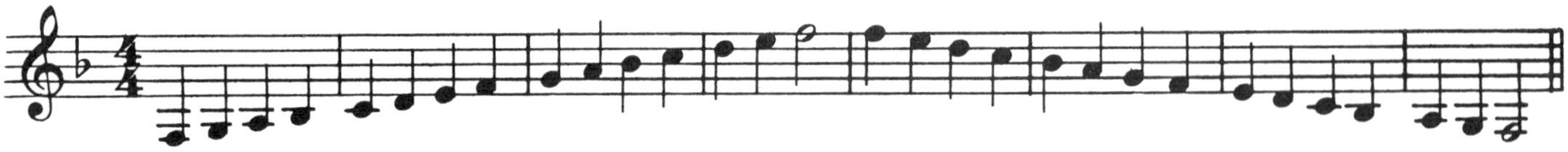

1.

2.

3.

OH! SUSANNA

4.

BLOW THE MAN DOWN

5.

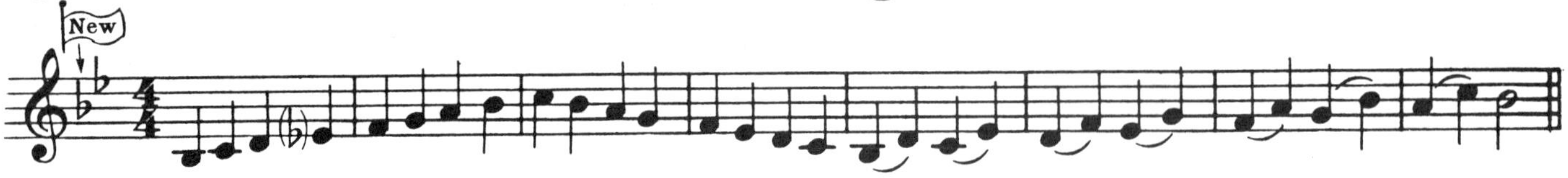

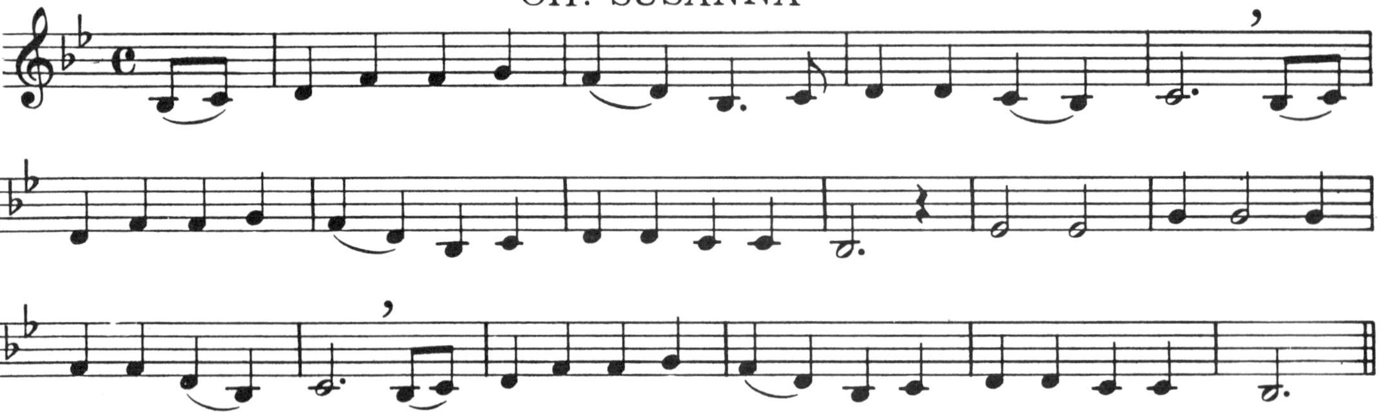

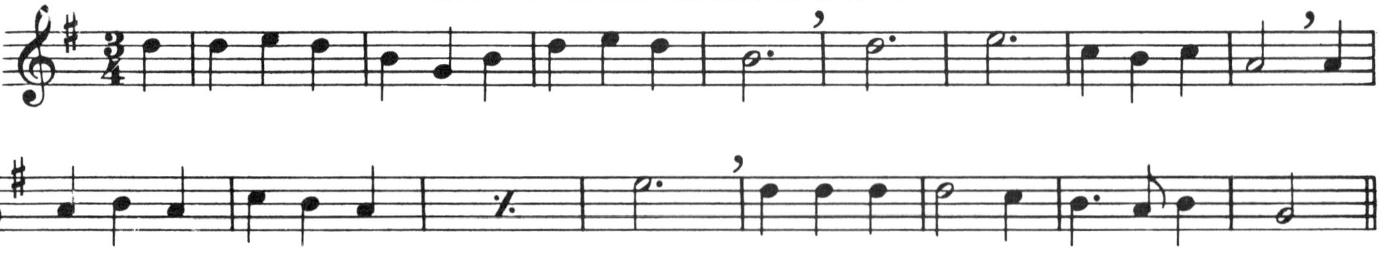

THE MARINES' HYMN (Duet)

6.

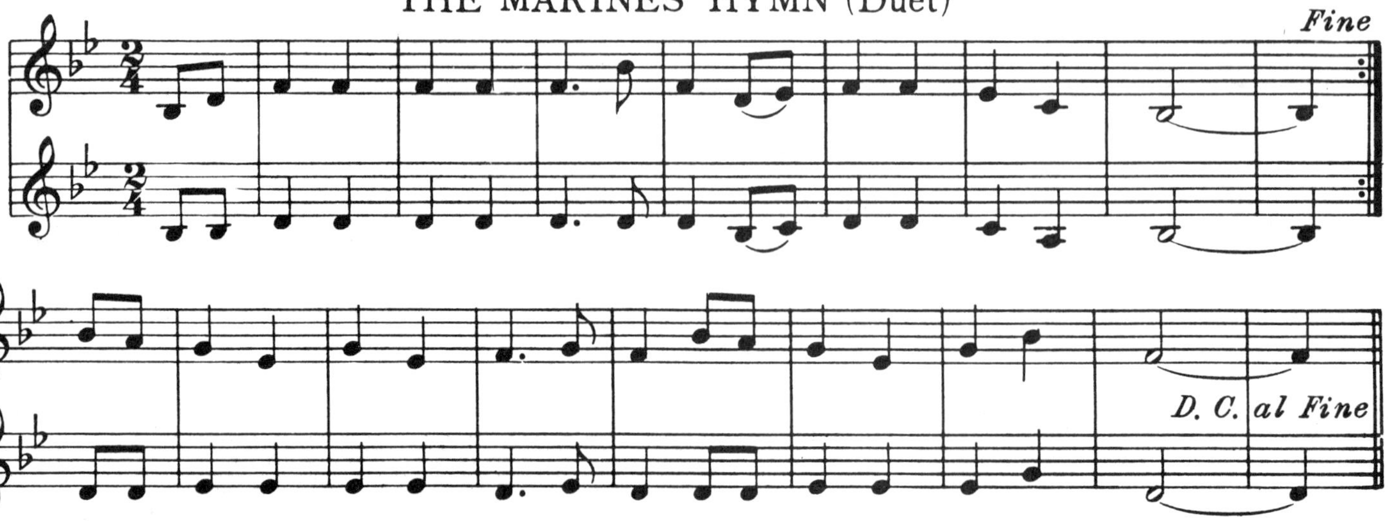

THIS LESSON HAS BEEN COMPLETED. DATE__________ EXCELLENT ☐ GOOD ☐ FAIR ☐

LESSON 22.

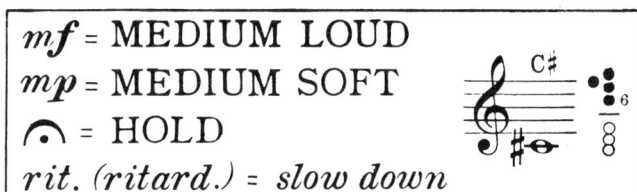

mf = MEDIUM LOUD
mp = MEDIUM SOFT
𝄐 = HOLD
rit. (ritard.) = *slow down*

C♯
6

AULD LANG SYNE

Traditional

1.
New
mf (medium loud)
New
HOLD THIS NOTE
A LITTLE LONGER
New
ritard. (slow down)

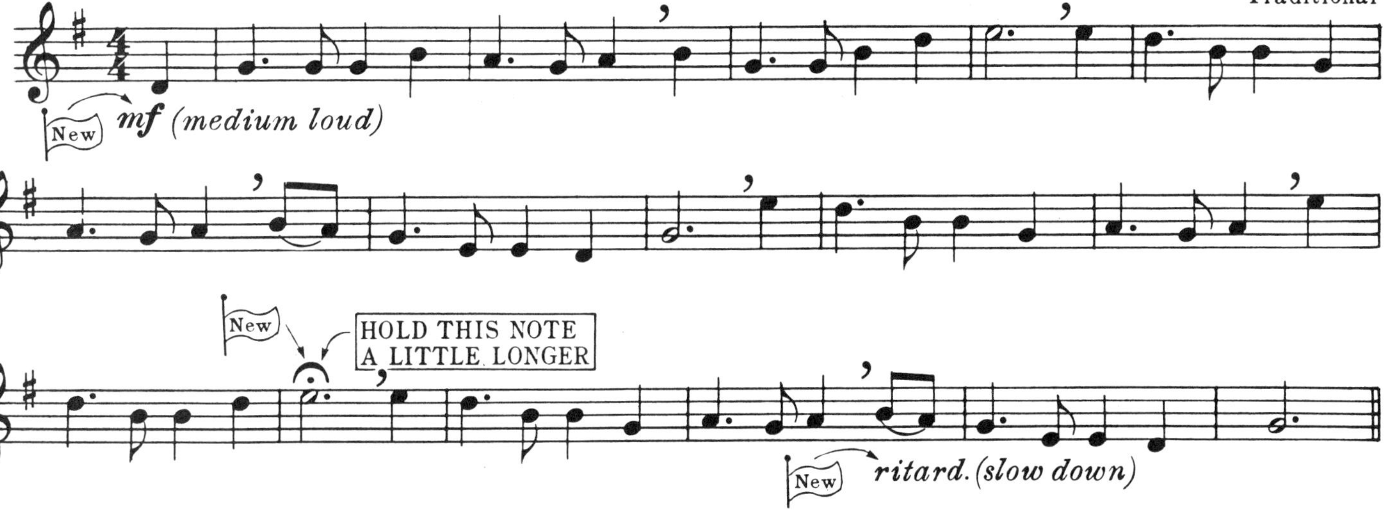

2.
f

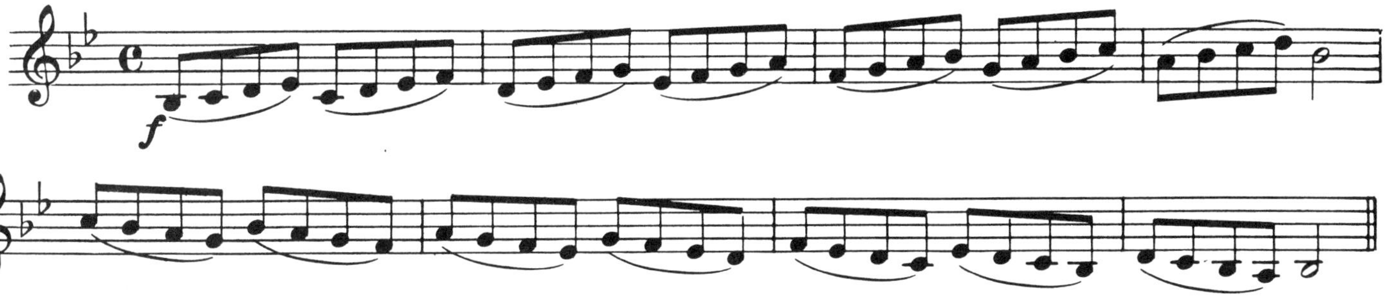

HYMN OF THANKS

3.
mf
rit.

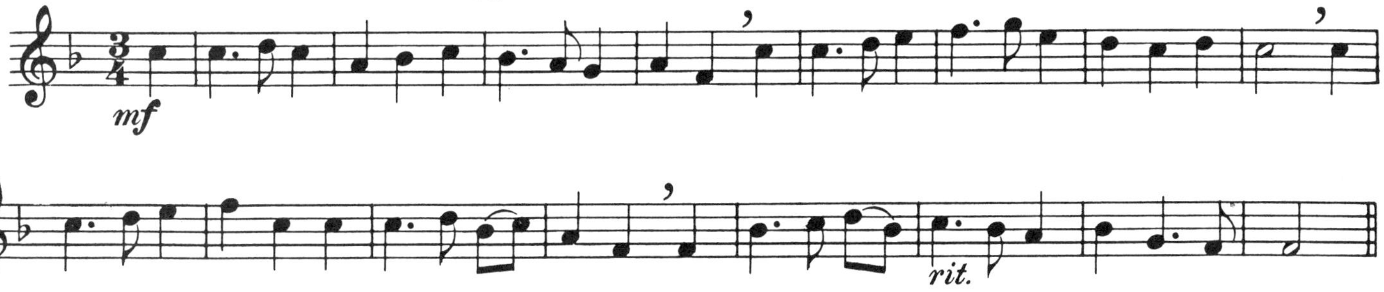

SONG FOR A DARK RAINY DAY

V. C. A.

4.
New
C♯
New
mp (medium soft)
rit.

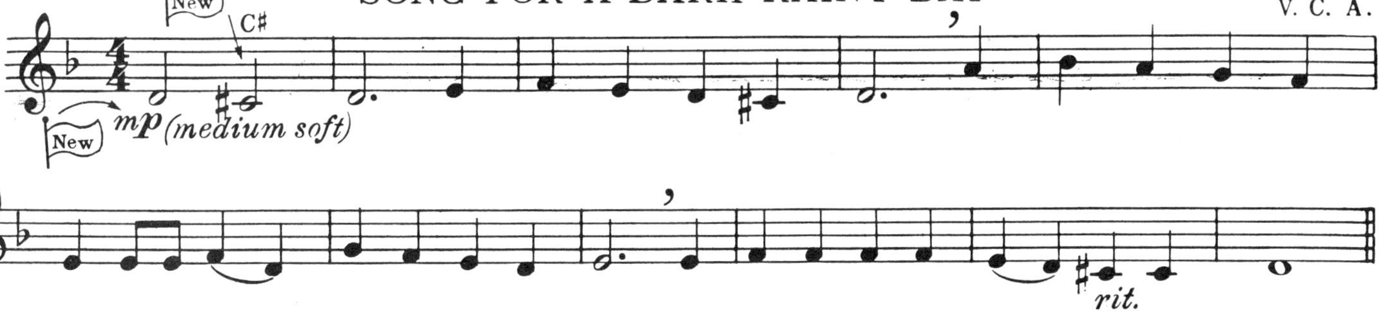

THIS LESSON HAS BEEN COMPLETED. DATE ____________ EXCELLENT ☐ GOOD ☐ FAIR ☐

LESSON 23.

SYNCOPATION

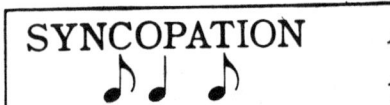

Allegro = Medium Fast
Andante = Medium Slow
Maestoso = Stately

1.

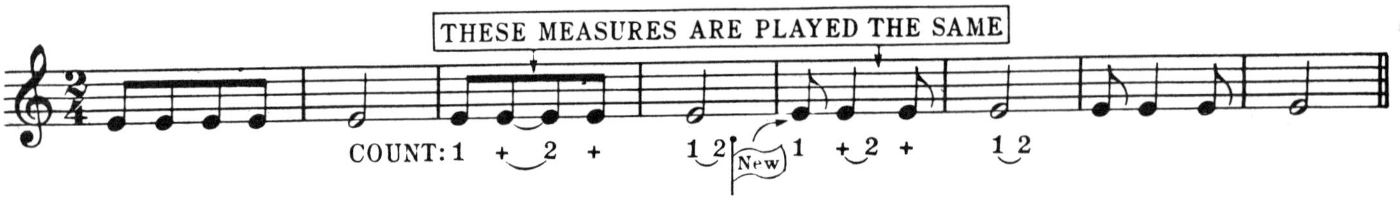

2.

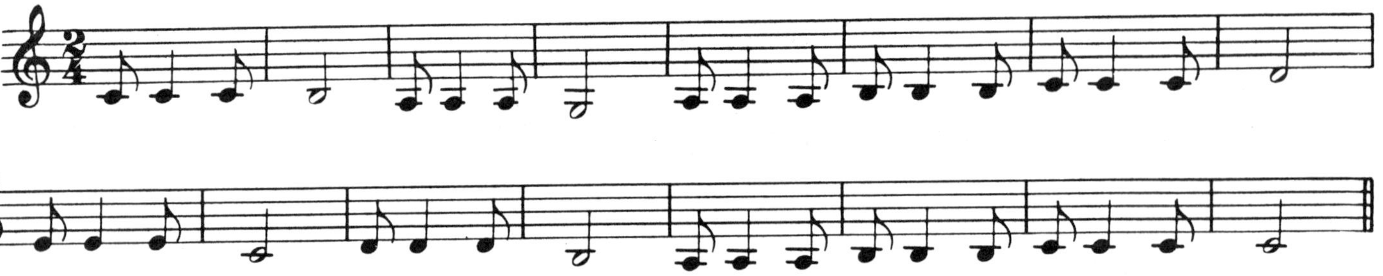

LIZA JANE

New
Allegro (Medium Fast)
Traditional

3.

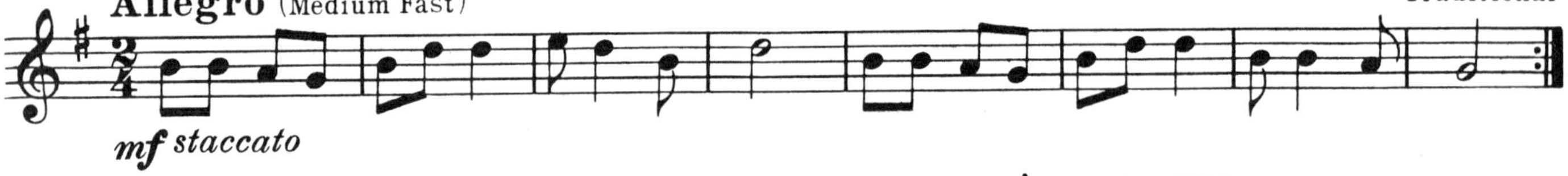

NOBODY KNOWS THE TROUBLE I'VE SEEN

New
Andante (Medium Slow)
Traditional

4.

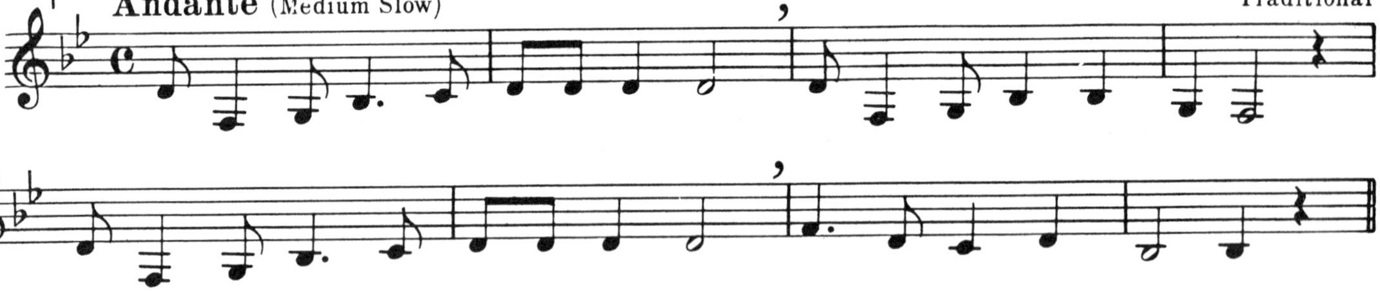

THEME FROM FINLANDIA

New
Maestoso (Stately)
SIBELIUS

5.

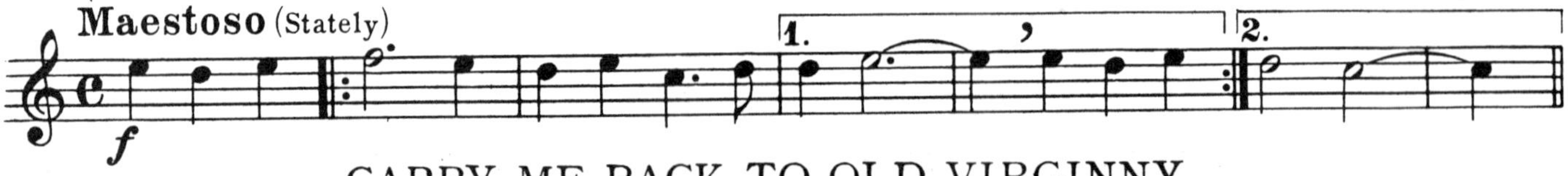

CARRY ME BACK TO OLD VIRGINNY

BLAND

6.

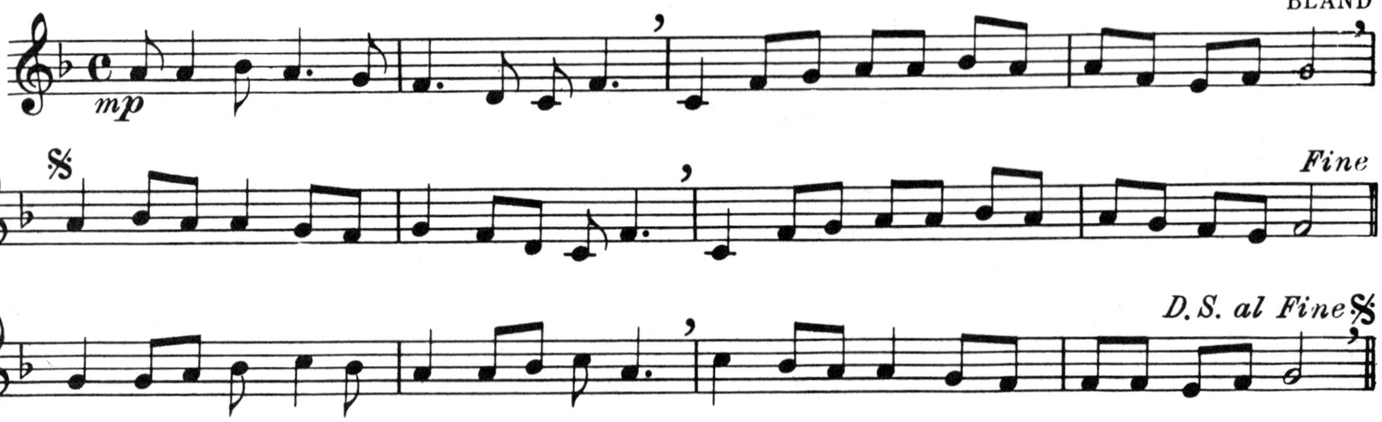

THIS LESSON HAS BEEN COMPLETED. DATE __________ EXCELLENT ☐ GOOD ☐ FAIR ☐

30

ELEMENTARY

*See Notes Below

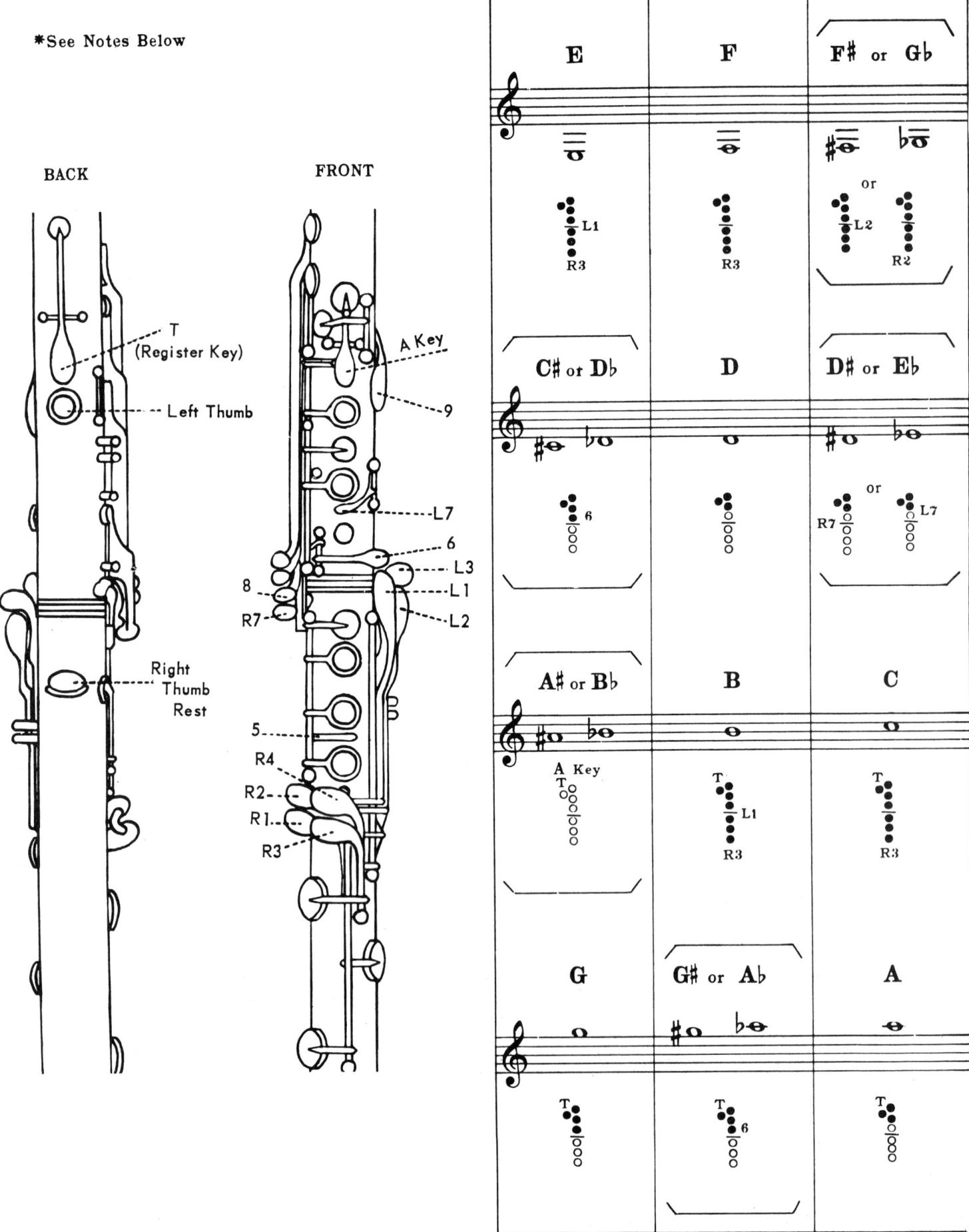

* When two fingerings are given for a note, the one on the left should be learned first.
Your teacher will tell you when it is best to use the other fingering.
When two notes are given together (G♯ or A♭), they sound alike and therefore are fingered the same.

21389-29

FINGERING CHART

The pieces on this page may be played as Solos, Duets, Trios and Rounds as indicated under each title. These Ensembles may be played by groups of "like" or "mixed" instruments (Flutes, Oboes, Trumpets, Drums, etc. may play together). When "mixed" groups play these Ensembles, only F Horns and E♭ Saxophones may be used.

*This Round is taken from "Supersound Warmups" by Andrew Balent.   © 1981 WB MUSIC CORP. All Rights Reserved